SPOTLIGHT ON...

Foreshadowing
& Flashback

NEW YORK • TORONTO • LONDON • AUCKLAND • SYDNEY
MEXICO CITY • NEW DELHI • HONG KONG • BUENOS AIRES

Teaching
Resources

Acknowledgments

"Sweet" by John Triska from TEACHING POWERFUL
WRITING by Bob Sizoo. Copyright © 2001. Published by
Scholastic Inc. All rights reserved. Reprinted by permission
of John Triska.

Excerpt from THE MUSIC OF DOLPHINS by Karen Hesse.
Copyright © 1996 by Karen Hesse. Published by Scholastic
Inc. Reprinted by permission of Scholastic.

"Wheels Willoughby" by Tara McCarthy. Copyright © 2004
by Tara McCarthy. All rights reserved.

ISBN 0-439-65984-1

Contents

The Tell-Tale Heart

A retelling of the story

BY EDGAR ALLAN POE

I can't say how the idea first entered my brain, but once it was there, it haunted me day and night. There wasn't any reason for it. I liked the old man. He never did anything to hurt me, and I wasn't after his money.

I think it was his eyes! Yes, that was it! One of his eyes looked like the eye of a vulture—pale gray with a film over it. Whenever it looked at me, my blood ran cold. I made up my mind to kill the old man and get rid of that eye forever.

I made my move slowly. Every night at midnight, I opened his door very gently, poked my head in, and shined a lantern on his vulture eye.

I did this for seven nights—every night just at

midnight. But his eye was always closed, so I could not bring myself to do what I had to do. It was not the old man who bothered me. It was his evil eye.

On the eighth night, I was even more careful than usual. I thought about the fact that I was opening the door and that he wasn't even dreaming of my secret thought. I had to laugh.

Perhaps he heard me. He moved suddenly. His room was dark, so I knew he couldn't see the door opening.

I had my head in and was about to turn the lantern on, but my thumb slipped on the tin switch. The old man sat up in bed, crying, "Who's there?"

I kept still, not moving an inch. Finally, I heard a slight groan, and I knew it was a groan of terror—terror in the face of death.

I knew the terror the old man felt and I felt sorry for him, although I laughed inside. I knew he had been lying awake ever since the first slight noise. His fears had grown ever since. He tried to tell himself, "It is nothing but the wind in the chimney... It is only a mouse crossing the floor... It is just a cricket.

I waited a long time, and I turned the lantern up a little bit. I was careful. Only a single ray shot out and fell on his vulture eye.

The eye was wide open! I grew angry as I looked at it. I could see it perfectly—that dull gray eye with an ugly film over it chilled my bones.

Then I heard it, a low, dull, quick sound. It was like the sound a watch makes when it's wrapped in cotton. It was the beating of the old man's heart. It made my anger grow, but even then I kept still. I hardly breathed at all. I kept the ray of light shining on his eye. The beating of his heart grew quicker and quicker, and louder and louder.

In the dead hour of the night, in the awful silence of that old house, that noise terrified me. Yet for a few minutes longer, I stood still.

The beating grew louder, louder! Then a new fear grabbed me. The sound was so loud that a neighbor might hear it!

With a loud yell, I turned the lantern up and leaped into the room. He screamed once, only once, before I dragged him to the floor and lay the heavy mattress over him.

I smiled. The deed was almost done. For many minutes his heart beat on with a muffled sound.

This didn't bother me. The sound would not be heard through the wall.

Finally it stopped, and the old man was dead. I

removed the bed and looked at the body. I put my hand on his heart and held it there many minutes—no heartbeat. His eye would not trouble me ever again.

I worked quickly but silently as I pulled up three boards from the floor. Then I slipped the old man's body into the space below and replaced the boards so well that no human eye could have found anything wrong. Ha! Ha!

Soon after I'd finished, someone knocked at the door. It was three policemen who said that a neighbor had heard a scream. I smiled and invited them in. The scream, I said, was my own. I'd had a nightmare. I told them the old man was away in the country. I told

them to search the house—search it well.

Finally, I took them into his room and asked them to sit down. I placed my chair on the floorboards above his body.

The policemen were satisfied since I seemed very much at ease. But then I felt myself getting pale. My head hurt and I imagined a pounding in my ears, but the policemen just sat there, talking and talking. The pounding in my ears grew louder. Finally, I decided that the terrible noise was not just in my head.

I tried talking more quickly and in a louder voice, but the sound got louder too. What could I do? It was a low, dull, quick sound. It was like the sound a watch makes when it is wrapped in cotton.

The police didn't seem to hear it, so I kept talking, even more quickly. The noise got louder.

The men kept talking. Was it possible that they did not hear it? No, they heard, and they knew! They were making fun of my terror.

Anything was better than this. I couldn't stand their smiles any longer. I had to scream—or I'd die. The noise got louder, louder, louder!

"Enough!" I screamed. "I admit it! Tear up the floor! Here, here! It is the beating of his hideous heart."

Excerpt From

The Music
of Dolphins

BY KAREN HESSE

I swim out to them on the murmuring sea. As I reach
them, their circle opens to let me in, then re-forms.
The dolphins rise and blow, floating, one eye open,
the other shut in half sleep.

Joyful with the coming day, I splash and whistle at a
milky sun. The dolphins wake and whistle too. They are
suddenly and fully aware. The ocean fills with their
sound. Flukes slapping. Quick calls rising and falling.
We slide under and over each other, racing through the
morning waves, riding the misty lid of the sea.

Three gulls sit on the soft shoulder of a swell. So
quiet, I come with my dolphin cousins, up from below,
and scare the bobbing birds. The gulls rise, screaming
mad. We laugh and laugh, bright beads of dolphin noise,

while above the birds dip and cry.

A cool wind tickles the swells and one free gull feather floats on the face of the sea. My dolphin cousin grabs it and darts below. Under she goes, then up again, faster, springing into the air. She passes the feather to the next cousin who takes her turn diving, running, playing with it. Their game spins me in the waves. The small hairs rise on my arms.

While we play, the old ones search for something to eat. They flash their blinding sound into a school of silver fish. As my dolphin family swims, mouths open, through the thick school, I climb out of the sea.

Standing on the small beach, the mangrove swamp at my back, I hear a sound over the rush and hiss of the tide, over the whistles and squeaks of my dolphin family feeding, over the splashing and tail slapping. I hear a sound pushing at the air. It beats like a giant heart. Airplane. I see it far-off, pressed against the roof of the sky. It growls a distant warning.

I turn away to feed on molting crab, juicy roots, ribbons of salt weeds.

The plane comes closer. The sound of it shakes my bones. My skin shivers, like an orca is coming.

My dolphin mother senses danger, my smooth, beautiful mother with her wise eyes and her spotted flukes. I hear her; she calls me back to sea. I want to go to her. I am afraid of the plane. But I must find water to drink first and give my mother more time to eat. She does not eat enough because of me.

I make my way through the wet and tangled roots of the mangrove, creeping toward the opposite side of the cay. I reach the long rocks where rain gathers in wide, deep pools. There is much water today. I cup my hands and drink. The water is cool with a hint of salt. When my hands can gather no more, I scoop the water into a shell, and when the shell brings nothing, I suck at what remains with my lips.

While I drink, the plane flies close again. No longer is it a distant gleaming. It comes too near. It is not like other planes, more like an ugly fish with spinning fins on its back.

Something drops from it. I try to hide. The wind from the plane makes my long hair fly. The mangrove pitches and roars. I am pounded by spinning air. The earth shakes and circles of sand rise around me. I sense the frantic whistle of my mother, but the sound is lost in the scream of the plane.

And then a man jumps out. He comes after me. I slip deeper into the mangroves. But the man is too big, too fast.

I cannot get away.

WILD CHILD FOUND ON ISLAND OFF CUBA

MIAMI, FL, DEC. 5 — "I thought she was a mermaid at first," said Lieutenant Junior Grade Monica Stone. "Her hair hung down to her feet and she was covered with seaweed." On closer examination the flight crew on the Coast Guard Jay Hawk realized they'd spotted not a mermaid but a human child.

Their mission started as a routine surveillance flight over the Cay Sal bank in the waters between Florida and Cuba. The crew, composed of Stone, pilot Nicholas Fisk, and flight mechanic Gary Barnett, had flown hundreds of search-and-rescue missions over this section of water. But this mission was unlike any they'd flown before.

After the initial observation of the child, the crew radioed Miami and awaited clearance to land. Hovering above, they videotaped the girl. "Gary threw the pump can out to her on a parachute. Pump cans hold food, blankets, first aid. Most people run toward them. This girl ran away, hiding in the mangroves. She had this really weird way of moving, like the ground was rolling under her feet. Gary climbed down and walked toward her, holding out his hand."

"She was so strange," said Barnett. "The way she acted. More like an animal than a human."

Once they got her aboard the helicopter, Stone wrapped the naked girl in a blanket. "She was making a high-pitched cry, like a seagull," said Stone. "Her respiration was odd, popping out of her, like breathing was something she had to remember to do."

Stone, a communications and public relations specialist, speaks fluent English, Spanish, and French. The child either couldn't or wouldn't respond to efforts to communicate in any language.

Her height and body development suggest a girl somewhere between the ages of eleven and sixteen years, said Stone. Her weight, in the vicinity of one hundred pounds, is at least ten percent hair.

"Most refugees we pick up look as if they've been at sea a couple of days. Their eyes are bloodshot. They're dehydrated," said Barnett. "But they still look human. This girl was streaked with salt. There were barnacles growing on her, for crying out loud. The condition of her skin—she had circular scars all over her face and body—she had to be living in the sea a long time."

"Mila [the name given her by the Coast Guard crew] is definitely human, but there's something about her, something wild," Stone said.

The Immigration and Naturalization Service; the Bahamian, Haitian, and Cuban governments; and a team of medical specialists working under grants issued by the National Institute of Mental Health are disputing custody of the newly discovered wild child, the second such discovery in as many months.

True wild children are a rare occurrence, said Dr. Elizabeth Beck, research professor of cognitive and neural systems at Boston University. "Feral children are an invaluable resource for studying the role language and socialization play in the making of a human being."

Beck has designed a unique facility at the Charles River campus to stimulate a "human" response in these children. She attributes the public's interest in them to the fact that wild children like Shay, the fragile girl discovered in Idaho's Salmon River Mountains, and Mila have much to teach us about ourselves.

On the short flight back from Anguila Cays to the mainland, the distraught girl kept thumping her cheek against the window of the Jay Hawk and squealing. Barnett used his hand as a cushion between the girl's head and the hard surface of the helicopter wall. Her squeal could be heard over the engine chop, like an animal crying.

"It was like she was calling to someone down there," Stone said.

Stone poured water into a cup and offered it to the girl.

"She touched the water from the tip of her finger, then touched her finger to her tongue," said Stone. "Slowly she extended her palms toward me, cupped, sealed tight. I poured water into her waiting hands and she drank from them."

"There was just something about her," said Stone. "From the moment I laid eyes on her I wanted to do things for her, give her things. She was visibly exhausted by the time we landed in Miami, but by then at least she understood we meant her no harm. Right before we delivered her to I.N.S. she leaned forward and studied me with one eye, then slowly turning, she studied me with the other. It still amazes me every time I think about it—the way she connected with us. I've never felt anything like it."

One

Doctor Beck says, Where is the ear?

I show a picture of the ear.

Doctor Beck says, Good, Mila. Where is the eye?

I show a picture of the eye.

Doctor Beck says, Good, Mila. Where is the nose?

I show a picture of the hair.

Doctor Beck says, No, Mila.

The nose is not in the hair. The nose is here. In front of the face. Doctor Beck shows a picture of the nose.

Doctor Beck says, Where is the nose, Mila?

I show a picture of the nose.

Doctor Beck says, Good. Good, Mila.

I like good.

Two

The helper is Sandy. Sandy says, I have a present for you, Mila. Sandy says, This present is to eat. This present is good fish. Do you want to eat this good fish, Mila?

I say, No.

The fish is not good. The fish is dead.

Sandy is not happy. I like Sandy happy.

 ## Three

Doctor Beck says, What is this?

Doctor Beck shows a picture.

The picture talks. It says, Girl.

Doctor Beck says, What is this, Mila?

I say, Girl.

Doctor Beck says, Good. Good, Mila. What is this?

Doctor Beck shows a picture.

The picture talks. It says, Boy.

Doctor Beck says, What is this, Mila?

I say, Boy.

Doctor Beck shows a picture.

The picture talks. It says, Dolphin.

Doctor Beck says, What is this, Mila?

I say, Dolphin. Dolphin! Good good dolphin!

I like to see the picture of dolphin.

Doctor Beck says, Very good, Mila. Tell me. What are you? A girl or a dolphin?

I show a picture. The picture talks. It says, Dolphin.

I say, Dolphin.

Doctor Beck says, No, Mila.

Doctor Beck shows a mirror.

Doctor Beck is in the mirror. A girl is in the mirror.

Doctor Beck says, Okay, Mila. Tell me, what are you? A girl or a dolphin?

I look in the mirror. I look at the picture. The

picture talks. It says, Girl.

I say, Girl.

Doctor Beck says, Yes. Girl.

Good, Mila. You are a girl.

 Four

Sandy is here. Sandy says, Look, Mila. I have a book. It is a fish book.

I come to Sandy.

Sandy says, Show me the tail of the fish, Mila.

I am showing the fish tail.

Sandy says, Good, Mila. Show me the big rocks.

I am showing the big rocks.

Sandy says, Good, Mila. Show me the sea?

I say, Sandy come.

Sandy says, No, Mila. Show me the sea in the book.

I want to show Sandy the good sea.

Sandy wants the picture in the book.

I show the picture in the book. I make Sandy happy.

 Five

I am going to see another girl.

The girl is little.

The girl is different, not like Doctor Beck and the others.

The girl is different like me.

I say my dolphin name to the girl.

The girl looks at me.

I say my dolphin name again.

The girl makes a laugh.

Doctor Beck and Sandy and the others like the laugh.

Doctor Beck says to the girl, Shay. This is Mila.

Doctor Beck says, Mila. This is Shay.

I say the word Shay.

Sandy writes in a book, Mila says Shay.

Doctor Beck says, Shay is like you, Mila. Shay is learning to talk. You and Shay can work together. Who can show me a thing we wear?

I show a picture of boots. I say, boots. I have boots. Doctor Beck says boots are for rain only. My ears like to hear boots all the time. I make my good boots to talk like the dolphin.

Doctor Beck says, Good, Mila.

Shay is not showing. Shay is not saying.

Doctor Beck says, Who can tell me what you do with a fork?

I show a picture of eating.

I say, Eat.

Doctor Beck says, Good, Mila.

Shay is not showing. Shay is not saying.

Doctor Beck says, Who can tell me what you do when you are cold?

I am watching Shay.

I am walking to Shay.

I am showing Shay a gentle hand.

Shay is a soft hair girl. Shay is a big eyes girl. Shay is a little little girl.

I am looking in the face of Shay.

Shay is not showing. Shay is not saying.

But I am hearing Shay with no words.

 Six

In the night, Doctor Beck comes into my room.

Doctor Beck sees Sandy is sleeping in the chair.

Doctor Beck says to Sandy, Go home. You need to sleep.

I say, Sandy wants to stay.

Doctor Beck says, No, Mila. Sandy wants to go home. We all need to go home sometimes.

I say, I am not going home.

Sandy is watching me.

Doctor Beck is watching me.

Doctor Beck says, Soon you will go home, Mila. Soon we will all move to a home together where we will eat and sleep and play.

I am happy. I am touching the hand of Doctor Beck. I say, We go home to the sea.

Doctor Beck says, No. Not to the sea.

I am not understanding.

Doctor Beck says, We go to a house.

I say, A house in the sea.

Doctor Beck says, No. Not in the sea Mila. A house here, in Boston.

I come to Sandy.

Sandy makes gentle hands on me.

I want to go with Sandy and Doctor Beck. But I want to go to the sea.

Sandy says, Let me stay with Mila tonight, Doctor Beck.

Doctor Beck says, Yes. Okay. If you want.

Stay.

I say, Another time we go to the sea, Doctor Beck. Yes?

Doctor Beck is a tired face.

Doctor Beck is a tired voice.

Doctor Beck says, Another time, Mila.

 Seven

So good.

I have Sandy when going to sleep. I have Sandy when waking up. I have Sandy to play all the time. Now I am not only.

Doctor Beck comes. Doctor Beck tells Sandy to give me a swimsuit.

Sandy says, Mila, you will like this.

Sandy says, Here are pictures of a girl getting ready to swim.

Here she is in her swimsuit. Do you want to swim like the girl?

I say, Yes!

I put on the swimsuit. The swimsuit is funny little skin clothes.

I put on my good boots.

I am ready.

I say, Shay can swim too.

We go to Shay and Doctor Troy.

I show Shay the picture of the girl getting ready to swim.

I say, Come, Shay.

Shay is happy. Shay is holding my hand. Shay is coming to swim with me.

Outside is good warm sun. No more cold.

Outside is many things to see.

Outside is good for to breathe. Good for to walk. Good for so many things to hear.

Doctor Beck shows me to go inside a very big house.

There is water in the house! I am hearing water! I say, Come fast, Shay!

Shay cannot come fast. Only hop, hop, hop.

I find the water myself. It is a bad smell. It is

a bad taste. But it is water!

I am jumping into the water with my clothes. I make dolphin talk. Squeak and whistle. I am laughing and splashing.

Sound is everywhere. Inside me, outside me. Good water sound in the big room.

I am moving fast and fast in the water. It makes my eyes to hurt but I am so happy to swim. I say, Come, Shay. Come in the water.

Shay is putting hands over her ears.

But Sandy comes in the water.

I am going around and around. So quiet, I come behind Sandy. I make a big splash and Sandy drinks the water and coughs.

I am laughing. The sound is going everywhere in the big room. I am hearing with good water ears every little sound.

A boy is coming into the room. He is tall like Doctor Beck.

Doctor Beck says, Hello, Justin. Doctor Beck is not looking at me. She is looking at the boy Justin. She is not touching the boy but she is with the boy. The boy is made very pretty. Good arms and legs. Hair is wet sand, like Doctor Beck.

I come to the side and splash Doctor Beck and the boy. The boy snaps at me like the angry dolphin. The boy snaps at Doctor Beck.

I laugh and laugh and swim away.

The boy goes.

I am splashing water on Sandy. I am so happy.

I say, Doctor Beck, I can stay here and sleep here in the water room with Sandy all the time?

Doctor Beck says, No. This is not a place to sleep, Mila. Only to swim. It is time to go back to the hospital. Come out of the water.

I do not want to go.

Doctor Beck says, You can come here again, Mila. I promise.

A promise is like a mother dolphin going away, then coming back with sweet fish for her baby. A promise is a good thing.

Sweet

BY JOHN TRISKA

Gina Lucci was my idea of the perfect sixth-grade girl: tall, brunette, and aloof. Best of all, she was Italian, so of course I loved her. Gina Lucci, Gina Lucci, I would breathe her name in and out as I walked to school each morning, imagining her eyes looking back at me, visualizing her walking with me in the field at school.

"I'm Italian, too," I'd tell her.

"Really?" she'd murmur, and I would say, "Sure. Burastero is my mother's maiden name. My grandmother calls me Giovanni."

Gina would smile and take my hand, and we'd keep walking out in that field.

The truth is, I was terrified to speak with her. Gina would lean up against the ball wall with her two best friends, her hands in the pockets of her short-sleeved jumper, rocking on her heels, staring out over our heads as if she was watching waves roll in on some Mediterranean beach, as if my buddies and I messing around on the field weren't there at all. She exuded independence. That's what made the results of our meeting such a surprise.

Thursday at lunch recess, Dave Frazell had finally had enough of my mooning over Gina. He grabbed me by the back of my shirt and shoved me into the hallway, practically into her as she and her girlfriends walked toward the girls' bathroom.

"John has something to ask you," he blurted, and gave me a final push and was gone. I thought I was going to be sick, but I was thrilled just the same. This was it.

Gina shrugged at her friends. Jane took Cindy by the arm and they left, giggling.

Then Gina raised her eyebrows over those big green eyes, and I knew this was the way it was supposed to be.

"Do you want to go steady?" I asked. I didn't like the sound of my voice. It kind of cracked halfway through the sentence. I wondered if it sounded like that to her, too.

"I've been waiting for you to ask me," she said. What? This seemed unbelievable.

"So you do?" I said flatly, trying to control my pitch. It sounded more like a confirmation than a request. I waited.

"Okay," she said. She looked over her shoulder at her friends who fell over each other in hysterics.

"Then it's settled," I said. "Bye!" I turned and bolted for the field, where Dave and the guys were tripping each other, calling each other wussies. They took me back with slaps on the shoulder. Casually scanning the playground, I spotted Gina and the girls in a huddle by the bathrooms. I wondered what she was telling them.

That afternoon I walked home with Sandy, my next-door neighbor. "Of course, you and I could never go steady," I assured her, "since we're neighbors and all."

"Gross. No way," she said. "Anyway, now you have to give her a Christopher." I knew about this. I'd have to act fast and buy a St. Christopher medallion like the ones they sold at McQuarry's Drug Store. They gave them out at church when you were confirmed, but I wouldn't get mine until spring, and here it was October. I planned to ride my bike up there this afternoon and buy one—the dime-sized one with the green enamel trim around it, to go with Gina's beautiful eyes.

"Are you going to kiss her?" Sandy asked me. She stopped and watched me.

I thought about it. "What do you think? Am I supposed to?"

She shrugged. "I don't know," she said, starting up the hill. I hated that about girls. Why couldn't they just tell you what you needed to know?

That night I carefully wrapped the St. Christopher and chain in the box they'd given me at the drugstore. I had to spread out a cotton ball to fit inside the box so the medallion would look just right. Then I made at least ten drafts of the note before I wrote it on the little card I'd bought.

"Dear Gina, for you on this great occasion." No way. Too formal.

"To Gina, who I love." Nope. Too serious. And too short. I didn't want her to think I didn't know what to say.

"To Gina, for going steady with me." That sounded like I was paying her to be with me.

I wanted her to know that I liked her a lot, and that I respected her. And something about our destiny, being Italians, together. I had it!

"Ciao, Gina," I began. "You are the one for me. I think you are—" and I searched for just the right word, finally deciding she was sweet, like candy.

Normally, I dreaded Fridays. Miss Campbell kept kids after school when they failed a test. She made us study right there in front of her while she graded papers, and when we were ready, we could take the test again, but we had to pass it before going home. I stayed after school every Friday all year, because Friday afternoon was when we took our spelling tests. It didn't matter how much time I spent studying at home. The next day I'd go blank. Miss Campbell was nice about it, really. She never made me feel stupid or anything. She just told me I had to get better at spelling, "one way or another."

"Whether we like it or not," she'd say, handing me a blank sheet of paper to try again, "people judge us by impressions. And the first impression we make when we write is how well we spell."

But this Friday morning I wasn't even thinking about the test. I carried the box with the St. Christopher, and the note tucked into the ribbon, in my lunch bag. I didn't want anyone to see it, because I didn't want anyone to force my moment. I wanted to be alone with Gina when she opened it, so I could see her reaction.

After grammar we had library. I knew I could find a way to be alone with Gina in the book stacks, and if not, right after library was recess. The way my heart was racing, I knew I had to give it to her by recess, or I'd never survive the day. Can a twelve-year-old have a heart attack, I wondered?

When we lined up for library I reached for my lunch above the coat closet. My bag had a hole in it—my pear was squished—and the box fell to the floor right next to Jane Macey. I picked it up quickly and shoved it into my jeans pocket, but it was too late. Jane was whispering to Cindy, and Cindy grabbed Gina by the arm, and by the time I got in the back of the line, it was over. She knew, and they knew, and half the class was going to know by the time we got to the library. I felt myself beginning to panic.

In the hall Gina, Jane, and Cindy stopped at the drinking fountain and leaned over it, running the water and giggling until I came up. They cut in front of me, and Gina pushed to the back, and there we were.

"Here," I said, handing her the box. "It's kind of

crumpled. Sorry."

"Hmm," she said, and then smiled, and ran to catch up with the line. I walked the rest of the way, hoping my heartbeat didn't show through my T-shirt.

We had to sit through a ten-minute lecture on the Dewey Decimal System, and Dave Frazell kept looking at me, then at the girls, then back at me. All I could do was shake my head at him. I felt hot.

Finally free to get up and look at books, I slipped into the closest stack, 921, biographies. From a break in the books, I looked across the library to the round tables, where all the girls in the class were crowded around Gina. She was unwrapping the box. A few of them reached over and held the medallion before I saw Gina looking at it closely. Was she smiling? They were all in the way.

Then she began on the envelope. Oh God, please no! Not here in front of everybody!

She opened the card and read. She definitely smiled! But then Jane grabbed the note from her and read it aloud, and suddenly all the girls were laughing and Cindy was pointing at Gina. My face burning, I turned and opened a book about Louis Pasteur, flipping pages and thinking I had to get out of there, somehow.

The bell rang and I walked right out the door,

passing Miss Campbell on her way in to pick up our class. "John? Where are you going? John?" But I was running for the field, relieved by the cool air on my face, heading for the big oak, racing for cover.

A few minutes later Sandy found me behind the tree, and I learned what had happened.

"Sweat," she said, handing me the St. Christopher on the chain. "You wrote you think she is sweat. Here."

I took the medal, studying the saint standing mid-river with his staff, protectively carrying the small child on his shoulder.

"She says it's over," Sandy said. "Sorry," she added.

"It's okay," I said, pretending that I really meant it. I put the medal in my pocket. Above us a scrub jay screeched. Far away there were kids shouting, and a whistle blew. "When the bell rings will you walk in with me?"

"Sure," she said.

We stepped out into the field together.

Wheels Willoughby

BY *TARA MCCARTHY*

ere it is springtime again, with all the noises that go with it—whoosh-thwack-whoosh-thwack of jump ropes, the SOCCO-yay of softball, and the whirr-squeal of bicycles. Another sound is the steady zhoom-zhoom of Rollerblades. Every spring, when people on our block hear that special Rollerblade sound, they say things like, "That reminds me of good ol' Wheels Willoughby" and "Has anyone ever heard from Wheels? I wonder what happened to her?"

Wheels was the fastest Rollerblader on the block. People say now that she could skate before she could walk, but that's not true. Wheels learned to skate right along with the rest of us, but she learned faster and soon began to go faster. When she was only eight she skated all the way from the South River to the North River—in five minutes flat. That's a mile a minute!

"You ought to have racing stripes on those skates," said Zack. "Wheels must be your middle name!" And that was how Wheels got her nickname, which we all agreed was much nicer-sounding than Wilhelmina.

Wheels was really okay about being able to skate better than anybody else. She didn't brag. She helped the rest of us increase our speed. She taught the littlest kids how to skate. She even repaired skates for other people.

Still, it was amazing to see Wheels on her Rollerblades and on her own. We liked to watch her circling the block like a puff of wind, or timing her skating so that she hit all the walk signs and none of the don't walk. As she sped uptown, downtown, and crosstown, she often had races with drivers of motorcycles, sportscars, and taxicabs. She always gave them a head start and she always won.

Wheels never had to worry about getting to the

park, or the museum, or way up to the stadium to see a ball game. Her Rollerblades took her wherever she wanted to go. Even going uphill was no problem. She got going so fast that she could coast uphill with ease.

Word of Wheels's skills spread around the city. One day Detective Sergeant Manero came to the door. "Miss Wheels?" she inquired. "I wonder whether you would do an exhibit of your speed skating for the benefit of the Police Department Hot Lunch and Choral Foundation. It's a worthy cause."

"Well, I guess so," Wheels said shyly. "The police have always been very good to me, after all. They've never given me a speeding ticket."

We all went to see the Speed Skating Exhibit. The stadium was packed and everyone clapped and whistled as Wheels tore around the outside track. The next day the newspapers called Wheels Wonder Girl and Super Skating Sensation.

"Wow!" I said to Wheels, "You're famous! People will start asking for your autograph."

"I guess we'll soon be seeing you on the Oprah Winfrey Show or at the X-Games," said Zack.

"Maybe we should start a Wheels Willoughby Fan Club," said Lucy.

Wheels was sitting there quietly, with her mouth turned down, spinning the wheels on her Rollerblades. She shook her head, "I don't want that. I just want to skate and enjoy myself."

Just then some members of the Senior Citizens' Committee stopped by.

"We'd like you to appear in a show for the Shady Elms Senior Residence," they said.

After that, the Animal Protection Committee asked Wheels to skate at the Canine Carnival. "You'll raise money for homeless dogs," someone explained.

And that evening, the president of the Billings Ball Bearing Company called Wheels. He offered $10,000 if she would pose for pictures showing her smiling at a Billings Ball Bearing and saying, "Boy, oh boy! Billings beats all!"

This sort of thing went on for many days. Sometimes Wheels would say yes, and sometimes she would say maybe and then say yes later on.

Finally, one Saturday morning, when the late spring sun was making tar bubbles in the street and the birds were quiet in the sparkling heat, Wheels said to us, "I've made up my mind about something. I'm leaving. I won't go to any more benefits. I won't

make any more guest appearances, and I don't want to pose for any more pictures."

"What do you mean, Wheels?" I said. "You're getting to be famous, and also rich."

Zack said, "Right, Wheels, and a lot of little kids are looking at you as their ideal. They're wearing *Wheels* T-shirts. You can't leave them now!"

"Don't forget," said Lucy, "you really are helping other people when you go to a benefit. Sometimes you even help cats and dogs. How can you even think of not helping anymore?"

Wheels sighed. "I know what you're saying is true," she said. "But I can't help feeling unhappy. Rollerblading is what I like to do. I do it for fun, in my own time, and in my own way."

Just then a committee for the Firefighters' Hook 'n' Ladder Hoedown came by. In not much time Wheels had agreed to make still another guest appearance.

We all went to see her that night. The firefighters and guests had a ball. And Wheels—Wheels was great. I've never seen her skate better. She whirled and swirled and steamed up one side and down the other of that ballroom. And then, when the applause had reached a roar, and the crowd was on its feet,

Wheels, with a shy little smile, skated once more around the room. Then very quietly Wheels skated out the door.

That was the last we ever saw of her. And that was many years ago.

Some people still expect to see her when spring rolls in with its Rollerblade sounds. And folks still have little arguments about whether Wheels was selfish or silly or sensible. And some, the young ones, aren't sure there ever was a Wheels at all. "How could anyone Rollerblade like that?" "Why would she leave if she was so good?"

But we know . . . we know . . . Wheels, we hope you're happy, wherever you are.

Spring Rain

BY SARA TEASDALE

I thought I had forgotten,
But it all came back again
To-night with the first spring thunder
In a rush of rain.

I remembered a darkened doorway
Where we stood while the storm swept by,
Thunder gripping the earth
And lightning scrawled on the sky.

The passing motor busses swayed,
For the street was a river of rain,
Lashed into little golden waves
In the lamp light's stain.

With the wild spring rain and thunder
My heart was wild and gay;
Your eyes said more to me that night
Than your lips would ever say....

I thought I had forgotten,
But it all came back again
To-night with the first spring thunder
In a rush of rain.